WH SMITH

SPELLING LISTS
for 8 year olds

Louis Fidge

Published exclusively for W H Smith by Ginn

Notes for parents

The Spelling List series of books is designed to help your children improve their spelling, and to fit in with the requirements for Spelling in the National Curriculum for English.

The books provide a framework of spelling activities for developing and practising basic spelling skills in an enjoyable and educationally effective way. The words taught are the sort of words most frequently used by children in their writing and take into account the Curriculum guidelines for English.

Ten Target words, containing the spelling pattern or patterns to be introduced, are highlighted at the top of the page. The activities which follow practise and reinforce the spelling in a variety of ways. Frequently Challenges are set to encourage children to think further or to use a dictionary. Test Yourself pages are included to check on spellings taught. As each page is completed get your child to fill in the Record Sheet on page 32 to keep a check on progress made, stimulate further effort and provide a sense of achievement.

Encourage your child to use the spelling strategy outlined below when tackling new words. Always offer positive praise and encouragement as your child is working through the book.

Notes for children

Follow these five simple rules to help you with your spelling.

1   **LOOK** carefully at the word you want to learn. Pick out any word patterns you know. Are there any smaller words within the word?

2   **SAY** the word. Does it sound the way it looks?

3   **COVER** the word with your hand. Try to see the word in your head.

4   **WRITE** the word from memory. Do not copy the word letter by letter.

5   **CHECK** to see if you spelt it correctly.

Target words

| best | cost | rusty | faster | interest |
| frost | last | just | mist | twisted |

1 Finish the words with **ast**, **est**, **ist**, **ost** or **ust**.

f____er tw____ed l____ c____ r____y

b____ inter____ m____ j____ fr____

2 Write the words.

ast words _____

est words _____

ist words _____

ost words _____

ust words _____

3 Use some of the words to finish the sentences.

Slow down! I can't go any _____.

The nail was very _____.

It's very cold. There's a _____ outside.

I fell over and _____ my ankle.

4 Instead of the **b** in **best**, write n, r, t, w, v and ch.

mother	father	grandmother	uncle	niece
brother	sister	grandfather	aunt	nephew

1 Write the words which contain **ther**:

_____

_____

2 Write the words which end in **er**.

_____

_____

3 Which four words are left over?

_____

4 • Close your book.

• Write as many of the words without copying
as you can.

• Check your spellings.

Challenge Can you spell the names of all your
family and relatives?
Write them below.

_____

6

Target words

fare	scare	made	glade	fate
care	stare	fade	ate	mate

1 Write each set of words in alphabetical order.

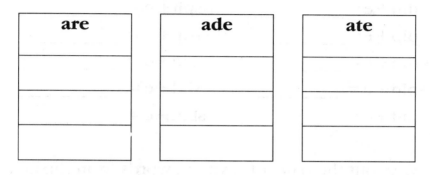

are

ade

ate

2 Write the word which means:

to frighten _____

to look closely _____

to get dimmer _____

a friend _____

3 Cross the **e** off the end of all the words below. Write the new words you have left.

farȩ = far   made = _____

care = _____   fade = _____

scare = _____   glade = _____

fate = _____   mate = _____

stare = _____   ate = _____

pipe	spine	ride	slime	spite
dine	grime	quite	stripe	slide

1 Finish the word sums.

din + e = _____   spit + e = _____

pip + e = _____   strip + e = _____

grim + e = _____   rid + e = _____

spin + e = _____   slid + e = _____

quit + e = _____   slim + e = _____

2 Write out the pairs of rhyming words from the box.

dine   spine

_____   _____

_____   _____

_____   _____

_____   _____

3 Look up these two words in a dictionary and write what they mean.

grime_____

_____

spine _____

_____

TEST YOURSELF

blind	stripe	quite	crunch	rusty
scare	bright	father	interest	aunt

1

Choose			Finish	Write
est	or	ust	r_____y	_____
est	or	ust	inter_____	_____
in	or	un	cr_____ch	_____
in	or	un	bl_____d	_____
fat	or	au	_____her	_____
fat	or	au	_____nt	_____
ar	or	br	sc_____ed	_____
ar	or	br	_____ight	_____
ite	or	ipe	qu_____	_____
ite	or	ipe	str_____	_____

My score ☐ out of 10

2
- Look carefully at the words.
- Close your book.
- Write as many of the words without copying as you can.
- Check your spellings.

My score ☐ out of 10

9

dress	hiss	fuss	boss	pass
cross	mess	miss	kiss	guess

1 Sort the words into the correct rows.

ass _____

ess _____

iss _____

oss _____

uss _____

2 Fill in the gaps in the table. Add some of your own words to the list.

verb	+ing	+ed
pass	passing	passed
guess		
	missing	
		kissed

Challenge How many more **ss** words can you think of?

10

Target words

oil	boil	tail	soil	sailing
nail	pail	hail	fail	spoil

1 Finish the words with **oil** or **ail**. Write the whole word underneath.

s _____   t_____   sp _____   p_____

_____   _____   _____   _____

n _____   b _____   h _____   s _____ing

_____   _____   _____   _____

2 Use some of the words to complete the crossword.

Across
1 Travelling in a boat
2 To heat water until it starts bubbling
3 A bucket
4 Icy rain

Down
1 To ruin
5 A sharp metal object

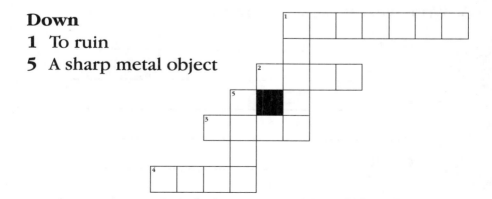

heat   boating   great   heating   throat

coat   floated   wheat   sweaty   moat

1 Finish the words with **eat** or **oat**.

m _____   c _____   gr _____   thr _____

h _____ing   b _____ing

h _____   sw _____y   wh _____   fl _____ed

2 Write the words.

eat	oat
1 _____	1 _____
2 _____	2 _____
3 _____	3 _____
4 _____	4 _____
5 _____	5 _____

3 Write what these words mean.

throat _____

_____

moat _____

_____

cheat _____

_____

layer	say	spray	playtime	clay
always	stray	delay	crayon	dismay

1 Finish the words.

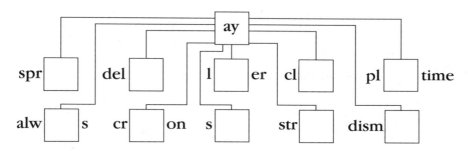

2 Write the 4 five-letter words containing **ay**.

_____

3 Write the 3 six-letter words containing **ay**.

_____

4 Write the 1 eight-letter word containing **ay**.

_____

Challenge Fill this box with other **ay** words that rhyme with **say**.

sweep	street	greedy	sleeping	bleed
sleep	creep	sweet	needed	deep

1 Finish the words.

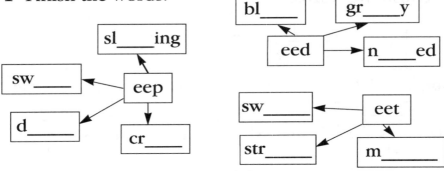

2 Write all the words in alphabetical order.

1 _____   6 _____

2 _____   7 _____

3 _____   8 _____

4 _____   9 _____

5 _____   10 _____

3 Use your dictionary. Put a ring around the correct word.

To rob   **steal** or **steel**?

Something you eat   **meet** or **meat**?

Part of a fishing rod   **real** or **reel**?

To make better   **heal** or **heel**?

An amazing deed   **feat** or **feet**?

14

would   should   could   because   behind

beside   before   below   beneath   between

1 Look at the groups of words below.
Underline the letter pattern common
to each group.
Then cover the words and write them in the space
underneath.

a would   could   should

_____

b before   behind   below   beside

_____

beneath   between   beyond   because

_____

Check your spellings.

2 Look carefully at this word.

beginning	

Cover it and try to write it in the box.
Check your spelling.

TEST YOURSELF

moat	stray	floated	would
crossed	beginning	below	could
	miss	because	

1 Find these words in the word square.

a	s	t	r	a	y	a	g	e	d
b	e	l	o	w	d	e	r	m	e
c	r	c	o	u	l	d	m	p	n
m	b	e	g	i	n	n	i	n	g
o	f	e	g	b	e	g	s	e	n
a	i	h	c	r	o	s	s	e	d
t	h	o	u	l	e	i	n	t	o
a	w	o	u	l	d	m	g	l	k
g	p	b	e	c	a	u	s	e	e
e	o	n	f	l	o	a	t	e	d

My score ☐ out of 10

2 • Cover the top of the page.
  • Write as many of the words without copying
    as you can.
  • Check your spellings.

My score ☐ out of 10

16

Target words

dead	bread	spread	thread	tread
read	head	lead	plead	dread

1 Write the words on the grid below.

	e	a	d
	e	a	d
	e	a	d
	e	a	d
	e	a	d
	e	a	d
	e	a	d
	e	a	d
	e	a	d
	e	a	d

2 Write the 4 four-letter words.

_____

_____

3 Write the 4 five-letter words.

_____

_____

4 Which words are left over?

_____

Challenge How many words can you think of that end in **eady**?

| dear | heard | earth | pear | heart |
| learn | spear | clear | bear | early |

1 Answer the clues.

Something that beats _____

A fruit_____

The opposite of late _____

I _____ you knocking on the door.

An animal _____

Our planet _____

A hunting weapon_____

Not cloudy _____

2 Write the word you have left if you take the **ear** out of the words below.

dreary   → _____

feared   → _____

wearing → _____

clearing → _____

swearing → _____

nearest → _____

3 Instead of the **f** in **fear**, write n, h, y, t, w and g.

18

found	ground	sound	bounded	wounded
pound	mound	hound	astounding	round

1 Underline all the **ound** words in the sentences below.

> I found a pound on the ground near a mound of grass.
> At the sound of my voice, the hound bounded round the corner.
> It was quite astounding that no one was wounded in the accident.
> A pound coin has a round shape.

2 Say these words out loud. Underline the one which does **not** rhyme with the others.

founded   sounded   wounded   bounded

Challenge Add **ound** to finish these long words.

ast_____ing   f_____ation   b_____ary

Look up the words in a dictionary and write what they mean.

1 Finish the words.

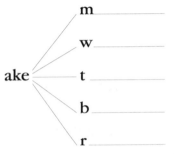 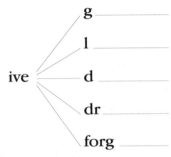

2 Write the words in alphabetical order.

ake
1 _____
2 _____
3 _____
4 _____
5 _____

ive
1 _____
2 _____
3 _____
4 _____
5 _____

3 Follow the rule: take away the **e** and add **ing** to the verbs below.

mak~~e~~ + ing = making   give + ing = giving

take   = _____   live   = _____

bake   = _____   dive   = _____

wake   = _____   drive   = _____

rake   = _____   forgive   = _____

20

Target words

tapping	popping	hopping	tapped	popped
hopped	begging	begged	sobbing	sobbed

1 Follow the rule: double the last letter and add **ing** and **ed** to the verbs below.

hop ➡ hopping   ➡ hopped

pin ➡

fit ➡

beg ➡

tap ➡

sob ➡

pop ➡

2 Fill in the missing word. Choose the correct spelling.

The frog _____ into the pond.
(hoped/hopped)

I _____ it would be a sunny day.
(hoped/hopped)

The man _____ the poster up.
(pined/pinned)

The notice was _____ to the wall.
(tapped/taped)

3 Double the last letter and add **ing** and **ed** to the verbs below.

stop ____   drop ____   flap ____   shop ____

windmill	snowball	handbag	wheelchair
bedtime	doorbell	teaspoon	blackbird
	classroom	breakfast	

1 Match and join the words to make longer words.

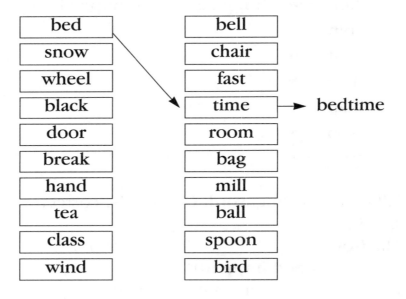

2 Answer the clues.

A bird with a yellow beak _____

The first meal of the day _____

A chair on wheels _____

A ball made of snow _____

A room where classes are held _____

What you use to stir the tea _____

TEST YOURSELF

read	earth	making	give
head	take	breakfast	early
wheelchair		astounding	

1 Write the words on the ladder on the left.
Put the words which you find easy to spell
at the top.
Put the harder words at the bottom.

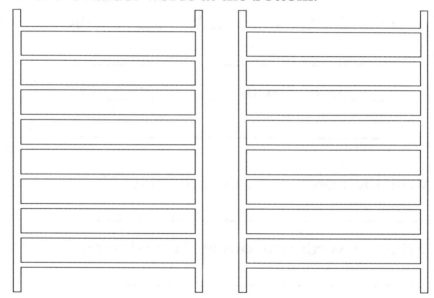

2 • Cover the ladder on the left and the box at the
top with a piece of card.
• Write the words without looking at the ladder on
the right.
• Check your spellings.

My score ☐ out of 20

23

shout   outside   south   scout   outfit

mouth   without   sprout   outing   about

1 Finish the words with **out**. Write the whole word underneath.

sh_____   ab _____   spr_____   sc_____

_____   _____   _____   _____

    m_____h   s_____h   _____ing

    _____   _____   _____

_____side   with_____   _____fit

_____   _____   _____

2 Write the words with **out** at the end.

_____

3 Write the words with **out** at the beginning.

_____

4 Write the words with **out** in the middle of them.

_____

Challenge   Write a sentence and use as many **out** words in it as you can.

24

Target words

right	might	tight	light	flight
sight	night	fight	bright	fright

1 Write the words you can make.

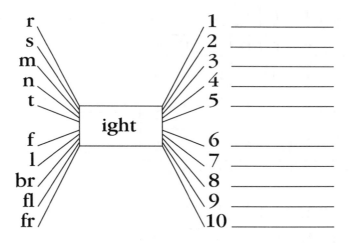

r
s
m
n
t

ight

f
l
br
fl
fr

1 _____
2 _____
3 _____
4 _____
5 _____
6 _____
7 _____
8 _____
9 _____
10 _____

2 Add **ly** to the words right, night, tight, light and bright.

_____ _____ _____ _____ _____

3 Add **er** to the words light, tight, fight and bright.

_____ _____ _____ _____

4 Add **en** to the words tight, bright, light and fright.

_____ _____ _____ _____

perfect   observe   kerb   term   perhaps

person   different   serve   river   under

1 Find, circle and write the **er** words in each line.

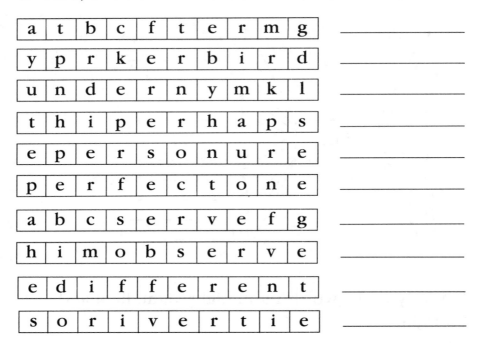

a	t	b	c	f	t	e	r	m	g	_____
y	p	r	k	e	r	b	i	r	d	_____
u	n	d	e	r	n	y	m	k	l	_____
t	h	i	p	e	r	h	a	p	s	_____
e	p	e	r	s	o	n	u	r	e	_____
p	e	r	f	e	c	t	o	n	e	_____
a	b	c	s	e	r	v	e	f	g	_____
h	i	m	o	b	s	e	r	v	e	_____
e	d	i	f	f	e	r	e	n	t	_____
s	o	r	i	v	e	r	t	i	e	_____

2 Which 3 words begin with **per**?

_____   _____   _____

3 Underline the tricky bits in the words below.

   different   difference   differently

Now try to write them without copying.

born	sort	thorn	ornament	comfort
worn	sport	short	morning	important

1 Sort and label these words into two groups
according to their letter patterns.

words with an _____ letter pattern	words with an _____ letter pattern
1 _____	1 _____
2 _____	2 _____
3 _____	3 _____
4 _____	4 _____
5 _____	5 _____

2 Write some other words that rhyme with **born** and
contain an **orn** letter pattern.

_____

3 Write some other words that rhyme with **sort** and
contain an **ort** letter pattern.

_____

4 Pick three difficult words from the box.
Try to write them here without copying.

_____

Now check your spellings.

Target words

window	below	allow	owl	flown
flower	grow	crown	cow	shown

1 Complete the words by adding **ow**.

gr _____   c _____   _____l   bel_____

    sh _____n   wind ___   cr _____n

    fl _____n   fl _____er   all _____

2 Write the words in two sets.

Set A where the **ow** sounds the same as in **grow**	Set B where the **ow** sounds the same as in **cow**
1_____	1_____
2_____	2_____
3_____	3_____
4_____	4_____
5_____	5_____

3 Find and circle some more **ow** words below.

d	o	w	n	a	b	b	o	w	l	c	d
e	y	e	l	l	o	w	f	g	n	o	w
n	a	r	r	o	w	h	s	n	o	w	i
j	k	p	o	w	e	r	f	u	l	m	n
c	r	o	w	d	o	g	r	o	w	l	p
r	h	o	l	l	o	w	s	t	v	o	w

Target words

card	garden	shark	mark	barking
hard	dark	orchard	yard	mustard

1 Finish these words with **ard** or **ark**.

c_____   y_____   d _____   b_____ing

sh_____   h _____   m _____   g_____en

orch_____   must _____

2 Use some of the words to finish the sentences.

I could hear dogs _____ in the park.

A _____ has sharp teeth and pointed fins.

We grow flowers and vegetables in our _____.

Cardboard boxes are made out of _____.

It is hard to see in the _____.

3 Look up the words below in a dictionary and write what they mean.

orchard_____

_____

yard_____

_____

enjoy	royal	boy	destroy	joyful
annoy	oyster	toys	voyage	employ

1 Use some of the words to finish the sentences.

I _____ riding my bike.

The ship made a _____ across the ocean.

The king wore the _____ crown.

When I am happy I feel _____.

I like playing with my _____.

An _____ lives in the sea.

Factories _____ many workers.

Peter is the name of a _____.

2 Write the **oy** words you have used.

3 Put a circle around the two words that rhyme in each line.

a loyal, royal, joyful

b employ, voyage, destroy

c oyster, enjoying, annoying

butter	rabbit	summer	dinner	supper
yellow	bottom	narrow	button	hidden

1 Join the syllables to make words.

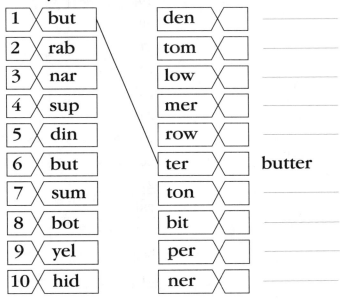

1 but	den	
2 rab	tom	
3 nar	low	
4 sup	mer	
5 din	row	
6 but	ter	butter
7 sum	ton	
8 bot	bit	
9 yel	per	
10 hid	ner	

2 Write all the words from the box which have **tt** in the middle of them.

_____ _____ _____

3 Circle the double letters in the middle of the words below.

suggest	success	bitter
rubbish	hammer	ladder
sudden	robber	winner

31

Record sheet

Page	Completed ✓	Page	Completed ✓
3	☐	18	☐
4	☐	19	☐
5	☐	20	☐
6	☐	21	☐
7	☐	22	☐
8	☐	23	☐
9	☐	24	☐
10	☐	25	☐
11	☐	26	☐
12	☐	27	☐
13	☐	28	☐
14	☐	29	☐
15	☐	30	☐
16	☐	31	☐
17	☐		

Test Yourself

Page	Completed ✓	Score (out of 20)
9	☐	☐
16	☐	☐
23	☐	☐